IT'S MINE

BY GINA AND MERCER MAYER

Reader's Digest **Kids**

Westport, Connecticut

My baby brother wanted to sleep
with my teddy bear.
I said, "No, it's mine."
Mom said, "Why don't you share
with your brother?"

I had to let my brother sleep with
my bear even though it's mine.

When I was eating a Popsicle, my dad
asked, "May I have a bite, please?"
I said, "But it's mine."
Dad said, "It's nice to share."
He took a *big* bite.

I set up my train. My sister wanted to
play with it. I said, "No, it's mine."
Mom said, "Let her play, too."

My sister took the tracks apart.

My sister was reading my favorite book.
I said, "That book is mine." Mom said,
"She won't hurt it."
I had to let my sister finish reading it.

Then I hid the book under my bed.

My sister was drinking out of my special
cup. I took it away. Dad said, "Let her
finish her drink."
I said, "But that's my cup."
Dad said, "Nice critters share."

So I fixed myself a drink in
my sister's special cup.
She didn't like that, but Dad told
her, "You have to share, too."

I went outside to play in the sandbox.
My sister wanted to play, too.
I said, "No, this is my sandbox."

Mom made me go inside.

I was playing with my building blocks.
My sister wanted to play with them, too.
I said, "No, they're mine."
Dad said, "There are enough blocks
for both of you."

I let my sister play. She knocked
my building down by accident.

So I made a dinosaur with my
modeling clay instead. Then my sister
wanted to play with the clay.

I said, "This is my clay."
Mom said, "If you don't share,
you will have to put it away."
I shared with my sister.
She made a dumb-looking bunny.

When I was blowing bubbles,
my baby brother wanted to
blow bubbles, too.
I said, "No, these are my bubbles."
Mom said, "Share!"

He dropped the bottle.

My sister wrapped her doll up in
my blanket. I took my blanket back.

She cried.

Mom said, "You don't even
like that blanket."
So I gave it back.
Mom said, "It's nice of you to share."

I caught a big frog in the ditch.
I showed it to my sister.
"Do you want to share?" I asked her.

She said, "Ugh!"
And she ran away.

I guess she didn't want to share my frog.

Well, at least I tried.